Read It!
Draw It!
Solve It!

PROBLEM SOLVING FOR INTERMEDIATE GRADES

Elizabeth D. Miller

GRADES FOUR AND FIVE

DALE SEYMOUR PUBLICATIONS

Pearson Learning Group

Project Editor: Carolyn Coyle
Production/Manufacturing Director: Janet Yearian
Senior Production/Manufacturing Coordinator: Roxanne Knoll
Art Director: Jim O'Shea
Cover Design: Alison Jewett-Furlo / Square Moon Productions
Cover Illustration: Stan Tusan / Square Moon Productions
Text Design: Square Moon Productions

ISBN 0-7690-0160-2
Printed in the United States of America
  4 5 6 7 8 9 10   05 04 03

This product is printed
on recycled paper

1-800-321-3106
www.pearsonlearning.com

Why This Program Was Created

Read It! Draw It! Solve It! is a unique problem-solving program designed for children from reading readiness through fifth grade. It was created to increase children's understanding of mathematical concepts through direct visual involvement. For each problem in the program, students will demonstrate their understanding of the concept by creating a drawing before providing the answer.

Students who use this program become confident in their reasoning abilities and are able to communicate easily their understanding of mathematics. When children work with illustrations they have made rather than abstract symbols, they learn to think of mathematics as problem solving rather than rote learning. They learn to reason rather than simply react, and they develop a better understanding of what they are doing. They also learn to read carefully because they know that they will have to demonstrate their understanding with a drawing.

Students love the open-endedness of the problems. The program encourages creativity in thought and expression, and it celebrates diversity. No two drawings will ever be the same, and many of the problems lend themselves to a variety of solutions.

Moreover, when students illustrate problems, the teacher gets a better understanding of their thought processes. If an answer is incorrect, it is usually easy to tell from his or her drawing where the student went wrong. Given the problem, "Nine people have come to the dance. Can everyone have a partner?" one boy made a picture of nine happy people in a row and answered "Yes." He had read the question as, "Can everyone have a party?" When his teacher helped him to read the problem correctly, he altered his illustration and answered "no."

How to Use This Book

Each book contains 180 problems, one for each day of the school year. The routine is the same throughout the program, although at the beginning of the year you will want to be sure to follow the activity with a discussion period to be sure any questions are answered fully.

Your task is simply to distribute the daily problem to the class and read it aloud if necessary. Students decide on the essential elements, make appropriate illustrations, and only then go on to provide solutions. Be sure they know that they are to draw the picture *first*.

Samples of Student Work _____

by Tracie Cannavaro

Octagons are worth ten thousand.   Hexagons are worth one thousand.

Pentagons are worth one hundred.   Quadrilaterals are worth ten.

Triangles are worth one.

Make a picture showing twenty thousand, two hundred fifty-eight.

Write the numeral. ___20, 258___

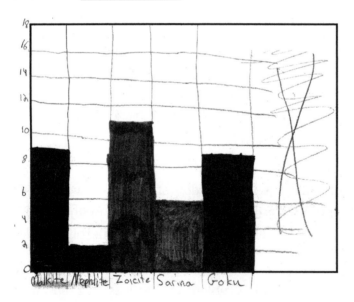

by Rae Moore

Write a story about the number of books read by five children.

Design a vertical bar graph to go with your story.

Malkite read 9 books. Nephlite read 2.
Zoicite read as many books as Malkite
and Nephlite read put together. Goku
read three less than Zoicite. Sarina
read three times as many books as Nephli

You may want to use this program as it was set up—one problem a day—or you may want to pick and choose problems according to the needs of your students and how they fit into your other curriculum areas. Note, however, that the problems increase in reading and mathematical difficulty over the course of the year.

Read It! Draw It! Solve It! can be integrated with any math or reading program. A blank template is provided for you on page ix to make up special problems for your class that incorporate specific information your students are learning.

What Your Students Will Learn

The format is the same as for the first through third-grade levels. At the fourth- and fifth-grade levels, however, problems are especially varied. This was done specifically so students will treat each problem as a unique entity and think for themselves about what is needed to solve that particular problem. Instead of a unit on measurement followed by a unit on multiplication, for example, students will encounter a fraction problem on one page, a measurement problem on the next, and so on. Some concepts that students will be asked to illustrate at this level are:

- alternate forms of representing whole number computation
- fractional parts of wholes and sets
- representing decimal parts of a whole
- simple percents
- getting information from and creating graphs and charts
- writing problems

Most students will be able to work independently most of the time. For example, the teacher may assign the problem for day 1 as independent work:

> Hexagons are worth one thousand, pentagons are worth one hundred, quadrilaterals are worth one. Make a picture of three thousand five hundred sixty-four. Write the numeral.

Even at the fourth and fifth grade levels you will want to be careful not take vocabulary comprehension for granted. Review each page before presenting it to the class, and be sure to go over vocabulary which may be difficult. The problem on day 70, for example, requires knowledge of triangles and halves as well as an understanding of the concept of symmetry.

Graphing is another concept students may find challenging. In the problem on day 82, for example, they are asked to write a story that goes with a circle graph. On day 32 they are asked to write a story to go with a pictograph.

There should be whole group discussion of these concepts before the students begin.

The following chart lists the fifteen math concepts that appear on fourth and fifth-grade mastery tests, with references to the pages in this book that provide practice problems for those concepts.

MATH CONCEPTS FOR FOURTH AND FIFTH GRADE MASTERY	PAGES WITH PRACTICE PROBLEMS
place value	1, 4, 13, 16, 24, 26, 27, 33, 34, 36, 37, 43, 44, 45, 46, 53, 55, 56, 57, 59, 61, 66, 75, 84, 85, 96, 97, 103, 107, 127, 140, 172
patterns	11, 23, 42, 52, 83, 94, 120, 178
fractions	5, 17, 28, 30, 47, 58, 60, 62, 68, 76, 77, 86, 87, 95, 98, 99, 105, 109, 110, 114, 115, 119, 120, 130, 134, 143, 146, 150, 157, 159, 162, 169, 176, 177
decimals	89, 91, 101, 122, 124, 151, 170, 174, 175
create graphs and charts	78, 116, 126, 135, 155, 158, 160, 165, 171
read graphs and charts	10, 22, 32, 41, 51, 65, 82, 93, 106
whole number computation	2, 3, 8, 14, 15, 16, 20, 25, 26, 27, 35, 45, 46, 54, 56, 57, 67, 69, 74, 75, 84, 85, 97, 107, 127, 128, 140
money	6,118, 33, 37, 48, 69, 71, 102, 160, 180
measurement	7, 15, 19, 21, 29, 31, 39, 40, 49, 63, 72, 79, 90, 113, 125, 141, 148, 154, 156, 170
write word problems	8, 10, 20, 22, 30, 32, 51, 65, 80, 82, 91, 93, 106, 114, 116, 124, 126, 139, 146, 153, 155, 158, 160, 162, 175, 176
geometry	1, 4, 5, 9, 13, 21, 31, 33, 38, 40, 42, 44, 49, 50, 60, 63, 64, 70, 73, 79, 81, 92, 94, 99, 125, 149, 154, 166, 170, 179
percent	12, 77, 80, 88, 100, 111, 112, 121, 135, 138, 139, 145, 148, 156, 163, 173
time	104, 136, 137
critical thinking	2, 6, 9, 14, 18, 25, 35, 48, 51, 64, 67, 70, 71, 73, 74, 81, 83, 90, 92, 102, 123, 130, 136, 144, 159, 161, 163, 172, 177, 178, 179, 180
estimation	7, 19, 62, 72, 90, 111, 113, 121

The program lends itself to all kinds of grouping. Whole class instruction is appropriate on some days, whereas on other days students may work in pairs, small groups, or independently. The format will vary from day to day, from student to student, and even from class to class. Some classes are ready for independent work before others are.

At the same time, it is routine that builds confidence. Every day there is a problem that must be read and illustrated—an intimidating idea, perhaps, at the beginning of the year, but reassuring later on. Children who were afraid to try in September are, by February, smiling, saying "I get it," and settling down to do the work.

The students also gain confidence when they are encouraged to be proud of their illustrations. Children are often pleased with their own work, and teachers and parents can build the students' confidence even further by collecting and displaying samples on bulletin boards and refrigerators.

Analyzing delightful illustrations is a lot more fun for a teacher than simply correcting papers. More important, the analysis helps the teacher to better understand individual thought processes, and then to provide appropriate encouragement and assistance. The better a teacher understands each student, the higher will be the student success rate.

Moreover, instead of "training" students in specific strategies, this program educates young people to discover what it takes to solve any kind of problem. Because of this approach, students who have tried it are not intimidated when confronted with novel situations. They learn to look for more than one way to solve a problem—and sometimes, for more than one answer. Perhaps the most exciting aspect of this program is that as students develop confidence in their reasoning abilities, they take this confidence with them into other areas of the curriculum.

Blank Template

Use the template on the next page to provide your students with special problems that pertain to the work they are doing.

Name _____

Dale Seymour Publications®

Hexagons are worth one thousand, pentagons are worth one hundred, quadrilaterals are worth ten, and triangles are worth one.

Make a picture of three thousand five hundred sixty-four.

Write the number.

There are 44 ears. How many dogs? How many legs? How many claws?

Using only red and green, make a picture of four different addition combinations which equal 18.

Blue beads are worth one thousand, green beads are worth one hundred, red beads are worth ten, and purple beads are worth one.

Add

two thousand four hundred thirty-six and

five thousand one hundred sixty-two.

Draw three rectangles.

In the first one, shade in $\frac{1}{2}$.

In the second one, shade in $\frac{1}{4}$.

In the third one, shade in $\frac{2}{4}$.

Show 2 different rows of coins, each worth $1.20.

Make pictures of things that are:

a. less than 5 inches long

b. between 5 and 10 inches long

c. longer than 2 inches

d. longer than 2 yards

e. over 10 yards

Write a word problem and make a picture to go with this equation.

$$9 \times 3 = \_\_\_\_$$

_____

_____

_____

_____

READ IT! DRAW IT! SOLVE IT! • GRADES 4–5

Draw a trapezoid that is made up of 2 triangles.

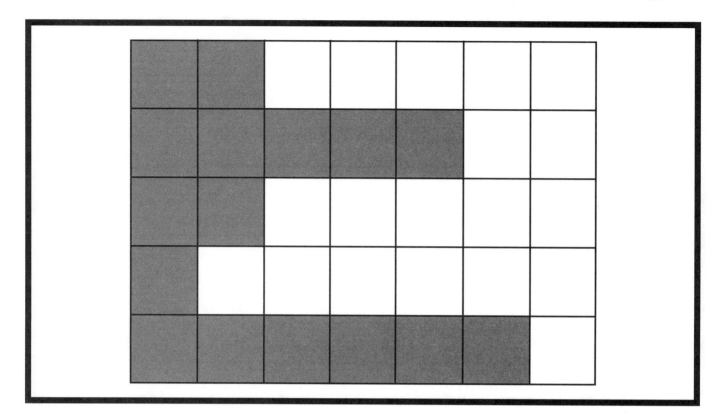

Write a story to go with this graph.

Make a pattern using birds, fish, and reptiles.

Then describe your pattern.

There are 12 people on each team.

The blue team has 25% girls.

The red team has 6 girls.

How many boys are on the blue team? _____

What percent of the red team is boys?_____

Hexagons are worth one thousand, pentagons are worth one hundred, quadrilaterals are worth ten, and triangles are worth one.

Make a picture of five thousand three hundred ten.

Write the number.

There are 33 wheels. How many tricycles? How many pedals?

```



```

There are 24 children in our class. We want each one to get
2 cups of punch.

How many gallons of punch must we buy? _____

If punch is only sold by the quart, how many quarts must

we buy? _____

Gold beads are worth ten thousand, blue beads are worth one thousand, green beads are worth one hundred, red beads are worth ten, and purple beads are worth one.

Make a picture of ninety-six thousand five hundred thirty-seven.

Subtract fourteen thousand two hundred sixteen from it.

Write the number.

Draw a circle divided into eighths.

Shade $\frac{1}{2}$ of the circle.

What other fraction might you use to describe the portion you have shaded? _____

Show 5 different rows of coins. Each row should be worth $1.83.

Make pictures of things that weigh:

a. less than 5 lb

b. between 5 and 20 lb

c. between 20 and 100 lb

d. between 100 and 200 lb

e. over 200 lb

Write a word problem and make a picture to go with this equation.

52 divided by 4 = _____

READ IT! DRAW IT! SOLVE IT! • GRADES 4–5

Copyright© Dale Seymour Publications®

Draw a triangle with a 3-inch base.

Draw a triangle with a 3-centimeter base next to it.

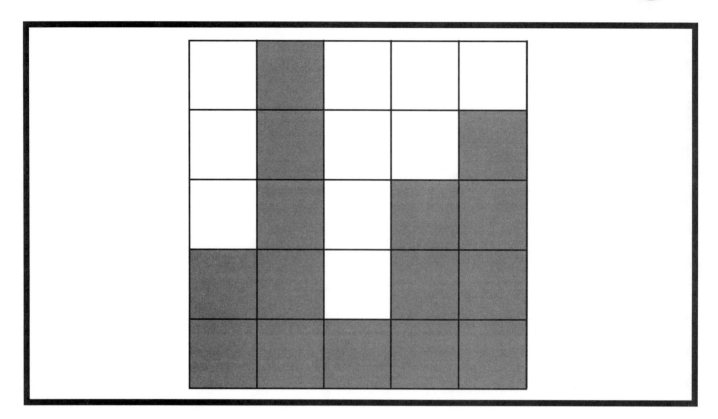

Write a story to go with this graph.

READ IT! DRAW IT! SOLVE IT! • GRADES 4–5

Copyright© Dale Seymour Publications®

Make a pattern using cubes of different colors. Use at least 40 cubes in your pattern. Explain the pattern.

_____

_____

_____

_____

Hexagons are worth one thousand, pentagons are worth one hundred, quadrilaterals are worth ten, and triangles are worth one.

Make a picture of seven thousand two hundred five.

Write the number.

Here are 60 fingers.

How many people? _____

How many legs? _____

READ IT! DRAW IT! SOLVE IT! • GRADES 4–5

25

(blank work area box)

Blue beads are worth one thousand, green beads are worth one hundred, red beads are worth ten, and purple beads are worth one.

Add together:

one thousand three hundred sixty and

four thousand nine hundred twelve.

Gold beads are worth ten thousand, blue beads are worth one thousand, green beads are worth one hundred, red beads are worth ten, and purple beads are worth one.

Make a picture of eighty-five thousand two hundred seventy-four.

Then show twelve thousand one hundred three subtracted from it.

Draw three circles divided into fourths.

Shade in different amounts in each circle and write
a fraction to tell how much is shaded in each one.

Make pictures of things you would use to measure:

a. time

b. liquids

c. a short distance

d. a long distance

e. weight

Write a word problem to go with the following equation.

$$\frac{1}{4} + \frac{1}{4} = _____$$

Make a picture to go with your problem.

Draw a triangle with a 4-inch base.

Draw a square with a 1-inch base inside the triangle.

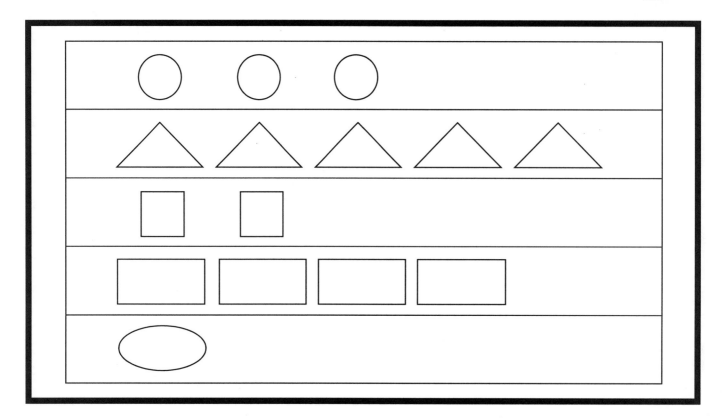

Write a story to go with this pictograph.

[blank box for drawing]

Create a pattern using octagons, pentagons, hexagons, and the colors red and green.

Use at least 45 shapes in your pattern.

Explain the pattern.

_____

_____

_____

_____

Hexagons are worth one thousand, pentagons are worth one hundred, quadrilaterals are worth ten, and triangles are worth one.

Make a picture of six thousand fifty-three.

There are 80 fingers.

How many right hands? _____

How many arms? _____

Blue beads are worth one thousand, green beads are worth one hundred, red beads are worth ten, and purple beads are worth one.

Add

one thousand four hundred seventy-six and

eight thousand one hundred three.

Gold beads are worth ten thousand, blue beads are worth one thousand, green beads are worth one hundred, red beads are worth ten, and purple beads are worth one.

Make a picture of seventy-eight thousand five hundred forty-two.

Subtract sixty-six thousand three hundred seven from it.

Draw three rectangles divided into fourths.

Shade in a different amount in each rectangle.

Write a fraction to tell how much is shaded in each.

Make pictures of things you would measure using:

a. inches

b. yards

c. kilometers

d. ounces

e. liters

Draw a triangle that is 4 inches wide at the base and $3\frac{1}{2}$ inches high.

Draw a $1\frac{1}{2}$-inch square inside the triangle.

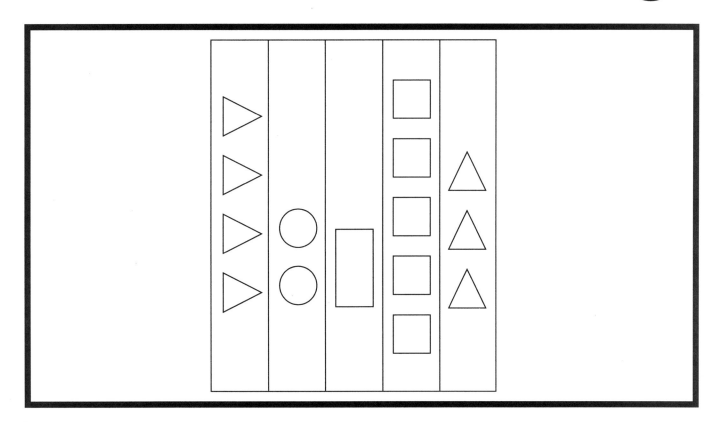

Make a picture to go with this vertical pictograph.

Design a pattern using two different kinds of shapes and the colors red, yellow, and blue.

Have at least 48 shapes in your pattern. Explain the pattern.

_____

_____

_____

_____

Evergreen trees are worth one thousand, fruit trees are worth one hundred, bushes are worth ten, and flowers are worth one.

Make a picture of seventeen hundred twenty-one.

Octagons are worth 8, pentagons are worth 5, quadrilaterals are worth 4, and triangles are worth 2.

Make 2 different designs each equaling 70.

Blue beads are worth one thousand, green beads are worth one hundred, red beads are worth ten, and purple beads are worth one.

Add

two thousand sixty-four and

seven thousand five hundred thirteen.

Gold beads are worth ten thousand, blue beads are worth one thousand, green beads are worth one hundred, red beads are worth ten, and purple beads are worth one.

Make a picture of sixty-eight thousand two hundred fifty-four.

Subtract fifty-one thousand one hundred three from it.

Draw three rectangles divided into eighths.

Shade in different amounts of each rectangle.

Write the fraction that tells how much is shaded for each one.

Show $1.76 using 14 coins.

Draw a triangle with a 4-inch perimeter.

Draw a triangle with a 4-centimeter perimeter next to the other triangle.

Draw three different hexagons.

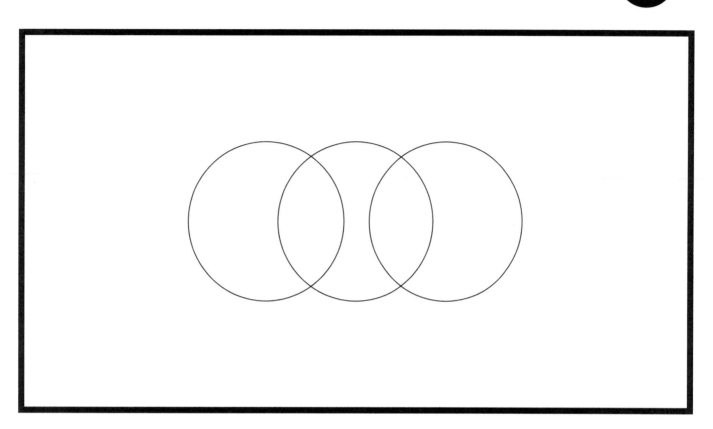

Write a story to go with this Venn diagram.

_____

_____

_____

_____

_____

_____

Draw 30 flowers in a row. Color them in a pattern.

The odd ones are blue or purple.

The even ones are yellow or red.

Describe your pattern.

_____

_____

_____

Octagons are worth ten thousand, hexagons are worth one thousand, pentagons are worth one hundred, quadrilaterals are worth ten, and triangles are worth one.

Make a picture of sixty-eight thousand five hundred twenty-one.

Write the number.

Show 30 marbles divided equally among 5 children.

Write the equation. _____

Octagons are worth ten thousand, hexagons are worth one thousand, pentagons are worth one hundred, quadrilaterals are worth ten, and triangles are worth one.

Make a picture of seventy-two thousand five hundred thirty.

Write the number.

Blue beads are worth one thousand, green beads are worth one hundred, red beads are worth ten, and purple beads are worth one.

Add

five thousand one hundred forty-seven and

seven hundred thirty-two.

Gold beads are worth ten thousand, blue beads are worth one thousand, green beads are worth one hundred, red beads are worth ten, and purple beads are worth one.

Make a picture of seventy-six thousand eight hundred sixty-four.

Subtract eighteen thousand fifty-two from it.

Draw nine flowers.

$\frac{1}{3}$ of them are daisies.

$\frac{1}{3}$ of them are roses.

The rest are tulips.

How will you be able to tell how many of them are tulips?

_____

_____

_____

Octagons are worth ten thousand, hexagons are worth one thousand, pentagons are worth one hundred, quadrilaterals are worth ten, and triangles are worth one.

Make a picture of sixty-five thousand one hundred six.

Write the number.

Using triangles show:

a. one third of six

b. one third of fifteen

c. one third of three

(blank box for drawing)

Octagons are worth ten thousand, hexagons are worth one thousand, pentagons are worth one hundred, quadrilaterals are worth ten, and triangles are worth one.

Make a picture of twenty-four thousand thirty-eight.

Write the number.

Draw 4 rectangles. Shade:

a. less than $\frac{1}{2}$

b. more than $\frac{1}{3}$

c. less than $\frac{4}{6}$

d. more than $\frac{1}{4}$

Draw a square with a 3-inch perimeter. Next to it, draw a square
with a 3-centimeter perimeter.

Draw three of the same shape. Make them different in size and color.

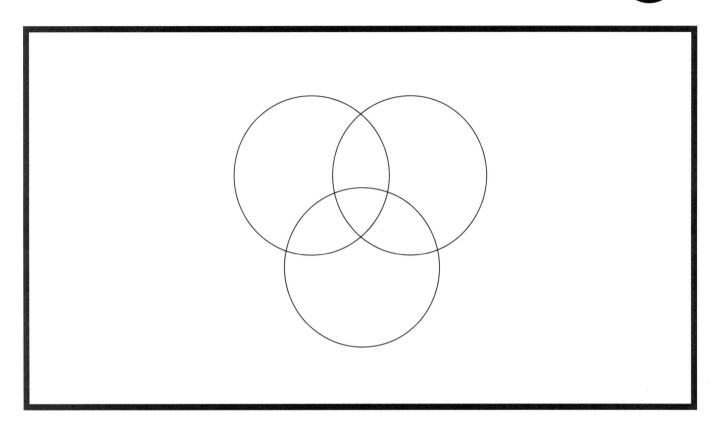

Write a story to go with this Venn diagram.

_____

_____

_____

_____

_____

_____

[blank work box]

Octagons are worth ten thousand, hexagons are worth one thousand, pentagons are worth one hundred, quadrilaterals are worth ten, and triangles are worth one.

Make a picture of forty thousand one hundred fifty-six.

Draw a basket with 30 pieces of fruit.

There are 3 pears. There are twice as many apples as pears.

There are $\frac{1}{3}$ as many bananas as apples.

There are 3 times as many peaches as bananas.

There are twice as many oranges as pears and bananas together.

The rest are grapefruit.

Draw sixteen balloons.

$\frac{1}{4}$ of them are red, and $\frac{1}{2}$ of them are blue.

The rest are yellow.

Write the fraction which tells what part of the group of balloons is yellow. _____

Write the number which tells how many ballons are blue. _____

Calculators cost $17 each. There are 23 people in our class.

How much will it cost to buy each one a calculator? _____

Draw two different triangles that can be divided into symmetrical halves.

Draw three different triangles that can not be divided into symmetrical halves.

Show $3.76 using only quarters, dimes, and pennies.

Make a picture of things you might measure in:

   a. meters

   b. decimeters

   c. millimeters

   d. centimeters

Give the approximate real-life length for each.

Make 3 shapes that are:

identical in color

different in size and

facing in different directions

[blank box]

We want to buy a set of dinosaur counters for our class.

A Tyrannosaurus Rex counter costs $1.50.
A Brontosaurus counter costs $1.25.
A Stegasaurus counter costs $1.00.
A Triceratops counter costs $.75.

We have $45.00 to spend. What might our counter set look like?

Gold beads are worth ten thousand, blue beads are worth one thousand, green beads are worth one hundred, red beads are worth ten, and purple beads are worth one.

Make a picture of ninety-five thousand one hundred twelve.

Subtract eighty thousand one hundred seventy-three from it.

Draw a rectangle divided into eighths.

Color $\frac{2}{8}$ blue, $\frac{1}{4}$ green, $\frac{1}{2}$ yellow.

Write 2 other fractions which could describe the portion that you have shaded yellow.

Draw ten triangles. Shade seven of them.

What percent of the triangles is shaded? _____

What fraction? Explain.

_____

_____

_____

On a circle graph show a number somewhere between 0.45 and 0.50.

Draw a trapezoid with a 5-inch perimeter. Draw a trapezoid with
a 4-centimeter perimeter next to the first one.

Write a word problem to go with this equation.

$$50\% + 25\% = \underline{\hspace{1cm}}$$

Draw a picture to go with your problem.

Make 3 shapes that are:

    identical in size

    different in color and

    facing in different directions

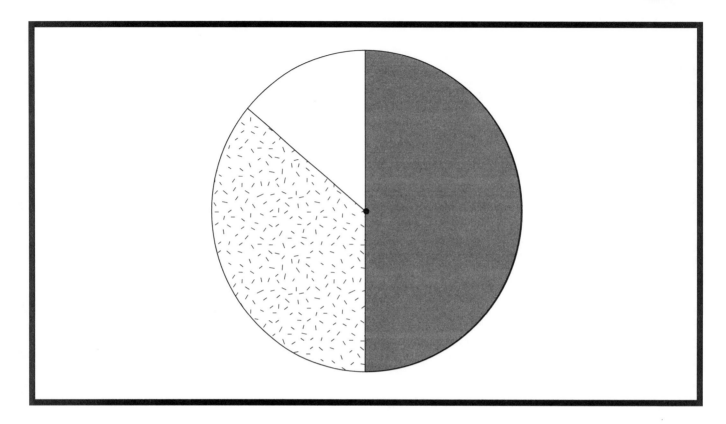

Write a story to go with this circle graph.

Design a pattern where shape and color are the same,
but size varies.

Blue beads are worth one thousand, green beads are worth one hundred, red beads are worth ten, and purple beads are worth one.

Make a picture of eight thousand three hundred sixty.

Add four thousand nine hundred seventy-two to it.

Gold beads are worth ten thousand, blue beads are worth one thousand, green beads are worth one hundred, red beads are worth ten, and purple beads are worth one.

Make a picture of thirty-eight thousand six hundred fifty-two.

Subtract thirteen hundred one from it.

Draw twenty-four kites.

$\frac{1}{8}$ of them are purple, $\frac{3}{8}$ of them are blue, and $\frac{1}{4}$ of them are orange.

The rest are red.

Write the fraction which tells what part of the group is red. _____

Write the number which tells how many kites are blue. _____

Draw two octagons divided into fourths.

In each one color $\frac{3}{4}$ red.

What fraction of the two octagons is not shaded red? _____

Draw a 10—by—10 grid and shade 64% of it.

Make a picture which shows 0.60. Explain.

_____

_____

_____

_____

Draw a picture of a one year-old child. Make the body about 2 inches high from hip to shoulder.

About how long should the arms be? _____

About how long should the legs be? _____

Write a story to go with the following equation.

$$35 + 0.45 = \underline{\hspace{2cm}}$$

Draw a picture to go with your story.

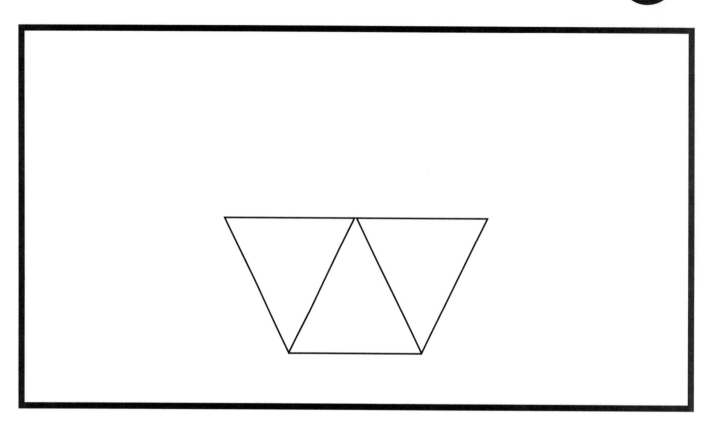

This is half of a whole shape.

Make a picture of the whole shape.

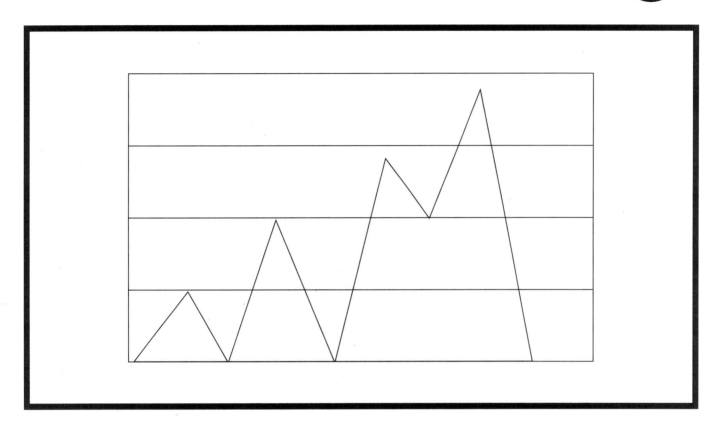

Write a story to go with this line graph.

_____

_____

_____

_____

_____

_____

_____

_____

Design a pattern in which size and shape are the same and color varies.

Andy, Bob, and Ezekiel each have 12 cookies. Dave and Cal have no cookies. Andy gives $\frac{1}{2}$ of his cookies to Dave. Bob gives $\frac{1}{3}$ of his cookies to Dave. Ezekiel gives $\frac{2}{3}$ of his cookies to Cal.

How can they make sure that Dave and Cal have the same number of cookies?

Quadrilaterals are worth one thousand, triangles are worth one hundred, circles are worth ten, and squares are worth one.

Make a design worth seven thousand five hundred sixty-three.

Gold beads are worth ten thousand, blue beads are worth one thousand, green beads are worth one hundred, red beads are worth ten, and purple beads are worth one.

Make a picture of forty-six thousand five hundred thirty-two.

Subtract eighteen thousand seven hundred sixteen from it.

Draw a circle divided into sixths.

Color $\frac{1}{3}$ red, $\frac{1}{3}$ blue, and the rest yellow.

Make two other circles that look just like the first one.

Write a fraction that tells what part of the whole group is yellow.

Use quadrilaterals to make a picture of $\frac{5}{8}$.

Tell what the 5 means.

Tell what the 8 means.

Draw a 10–by–10 grid. Shade 18% of it.

Divide your paper in half.

On the left side, make a picture of less than 0.50.

On the right side, make a picture of more than 0.50.

Show $4.78 using only half-dollars, nickels, and pennies.

Hexagons are worth ten thousand, octagons are worth one thousand, triangles are worth one hundred, squares are worth ten, and circles are worth one.

Make two different designs, each worth sixty-five thousand eight hundred twenty-three.

Draw a clockface which shows the time when you arrive at school.

Next to it draw a clock which shows the time 35 minutes later.

Write the time under each clock.

Write a word problem for the following expression.

$\frac{1}{2}$ divided by $\frac{1}{4}$

_____

_____

_____

_____

Draw a picture to go with your problem.

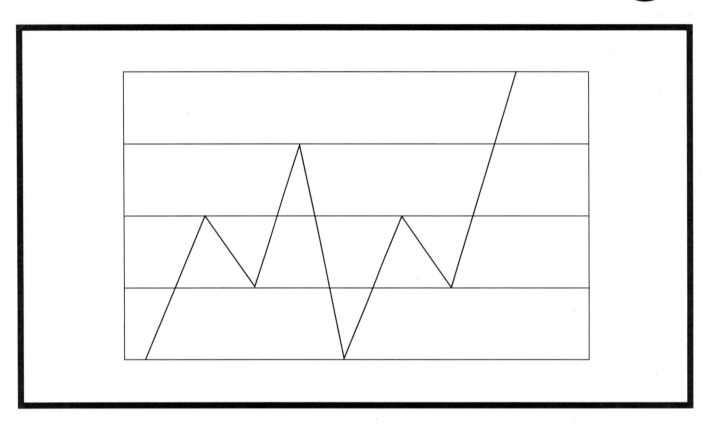

Write a story to go with this line graph.

_____

_____

_____

_____

_____

_____

_____

_____

Blue beads are worth one thousand, green beads are worth one hundred, red beads are worth ten, and purple beads are worth one.

Add

three thousand fifty-nine and

two thousand nine hundred eighty-six.

Gold beads are worth ten thousand, blue beads are worth one thousand, green beads are worth one hundred, red beads are worth ten, and purple beads are worth one.

Make a picture of fifty-six thousand one hundred twenty.

Subtract forty-eight thousand nine hundred thirteen from it.

Show $\frac{3}{6}$ of a rectangle.

Show $\frac{3}{6}$ of a set of trees.

Describe your drawings.

_____

_____

_____

_____

_____

_____

Use squares to show $3\frac{2}{3}$.

Draw jars that are about 33% full, 40% full, 20% full, and 75% full.

Under each one, write a fraction that describes about how empty each jar is.

Draw a picture of 10 circles.

Color 40% of them red.

Color 30% of them blue.

Draw a picture of a 12-year-old person. Make the body about 3 inches high from hip to shoulder.

About how long should the arms be? _____

About how long should the legs be? _____

Write a problem to go with this equation.

$$\frac{1}{3} \times \frac{2}{3} = \underline{\hspace{1.5cm}}$$

_____

_____

_____

Draw a picture to go with your problem.

This is $\frac{1}{4}$ of a whole shape.

Draw a picture of the whole shape.

Write a story about favorite colors.
Then design a horizontal bar graph to go with it.

_____

_____

_____

_____

_____

_____

Blue beads are worth one thousand, green beads are worth one hundred, red beads are worth ten, and purple beads are worth one.

Add

eight thousand four hundred thirty-six and

two hundred ninety-eight.

Gold beads are worth ten thousand, blue beads are worth one thousand, green beads are worth one hundred, red beads are worth ten, and purple beads are worth one.

Make a picture of forty-nine thousand two hundred three.

Subtract thirty-eight thousand nine hundred eighty-four from it.

Draw a train. $\frac{3}{8}$ of the train carries passengers and $\frac{3}{8}$ carries furniture.

Write fractions which might describe the rest of the train. _____

What might it be used for?

_____

_____

Describe the train.

_____

_____

_____

Draw 3 circles and shade:

a. $\frac{1}{2}$

b. $\frac{2}{4}$

c. $\frac{4}{8}$

If you continue this pattern, what fraction would come next? _____

Draw an array of flowers. Make about 30% of them red.

What percent of the flowers is not red?

Draw 18 kites. Make 90% of them green.

Write the decimal representing the kites that are not green.

Draw:

a. a rectangle with a 2-centimeter base

b. a rectangle which is three times as large as the first one

c. a rectangle which is half as large as the second one

Write a problem to go with this equation.

6 x 0.15 = _____

_____

_____

_____

Make a picture to go with your problem.

Draw a trapezoid with an 8-inch perimeter.

Write a story about the number of books read by five children.

Design a vertical bar graph to go with it.

Blue stars are worth ten thousand, red stars are worth one thousand, purple stars are worth one hundred, red beads are worth ten, and green stars are worth one.

Add

   forty-five thousand two hundred sixty and

   fifty-one thousand six hundred twenty-nine.

Pentagons are worth ten thousand, octagons are worth one thousand, triangles are worth one hundred, quadrilaterals are worth ten, and hexagons are worth one.

Add

sixty-seven thousand two hundred eighty-three and

forty-nine thousand one hundred seventy-four.

Gold beads are worth ten thousand, blue beads are worth one thousand, green beads are worth one hundred, red beads are worth ten, and purple beads are worth one.

Make a picture of fifty-one thousand sixty-four.

Subtract forty-nine thousand four hundred thirty-seven from it.

Draw a picture of 4 fractions whose sum is between 1 and 2.

Gold beads are worth ten thousand, blue beads are worth one thousand, green beads are worth one hundred, red beads are worth ten, and purple beads are worth one.

Draw a picture of each of the following numbers. Then add to

find the sum.

forty-six thousand one hundred twenty-five

fifty-one thousand seven hundred one

Gold beads are worth ten thousand, blue beads are worth one thousand, green beads are worth one hundred, red beads are worth ten, and purple beads are worth one.

Draw a picture of each of the following. Then add to

find the sum.

seventy six thousand eight hundred forty

nineteen thousand three hundred sixty-four

Gold beads are worth ten thousand, blue beads are worth one thousand, green beads are worth one hundred, red beads are worth ten, and purple beads are worth one.

Draw a picture of ninety thousand eight hundred twelve.

Subtract seventy-nine thousand one hundred sixty-three from it.

Draw a rectangle. Shade $\frac{1}{2}$ of it.

Draw three more rectangles of the same size.

Divide each one into a different number of equal parts so that you can shade the same amount as you did in the original rectangle.

Make a circle graph. Shade between 55% and 60% of it.

Draw a picture of something you do for about $2\frac{1}{2}$ hours a day.
Explain your answer.

_____

_____

_____

Draw a picture of something you do for about half that amount of time.
Explain your answer.

_____

_____

_____

Draw a circle graph that shows a 24-hour period in your life.

Label each section of your graph. Color it, if you wish to.

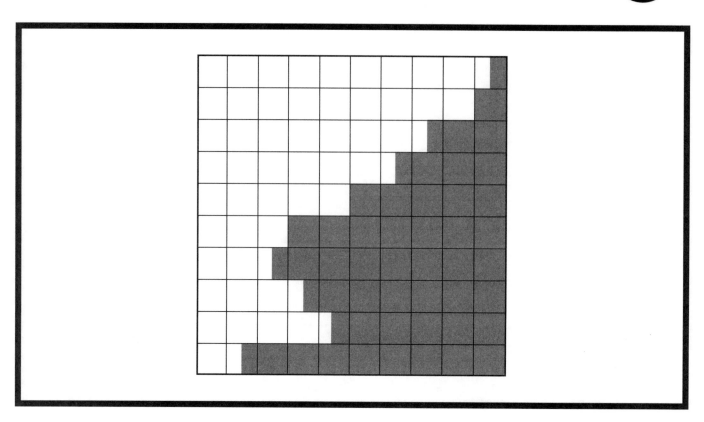

What percent of the grid is shaded? _____

Explain how you found your answer.

_____

_____

_____

Write a word problem to go with this equation.

24% x 12 = _____

_____

_____

_____

_____

Draw a picture to go with your problem.

Parallelograms are worth ten thousand, hexagons are worth one thousand, pentagons are worth one hundred, triangles are worth ten, and circles are worth one.

Add together:

sixty-two thousand fifty-one and

thirteen thousand seven hundred twenty-eight.

A hummingbird weighs $\frac{1}{12}$ of a pound. A toad weighs $\frac{1}{4}$ of a pound. A canary weighs $\frac{1}{3}$ of a pound. A frog weighs $\frac{1}{2}$ of a pound. A bat weighs one pound.

A bat, 2 canaries, 11 hummingbirds, and 3 frogs sit on one side of the seesaw.

Two toads sit on the other side of the seesaw.

How can we make the seesaw balance?

(blank box)

Gold beads are worth ten thousand, blue beads are worth one thousand, green beads are worth one hundred, red beads are worth ten, and purple beads are worth one.

Add together:

fifty thousand four hundred thirty-one and

seventeen thousand five hundred sixteen.

Use circles to show $2\frac{1}{4}$.

Draw a picture of 4 fractions whose sum is between 1 and 2.

Divide the box above in half.

On the left side make a picture that shows more than 30%.

On the right side make a picture that shows less than 80%.

Write a word problem to go with this equation.

$$\frac{1}{4} \times \frac{1}{2} = \underline{\hspace{1cm}}$$

_____

_____

Draw a picture to go with your problem.

Gold stars are worth ten thousand, blue stars are worth one thousand, green stars are worth one hundred, red stars are worth ten, and purple stars are worth one.

Make a picture of seventy-one thousand five hundred thirty-six.

Subtract nine thousand four hundred eighty-three from it.

Draw a circle with a 5-inch diameter. Shade 25% of it.

Use hexagons to make a picture of any fraction.

Explain your picture.

Make a picture of two fractions whose difference is $\frac{1}{2}$.

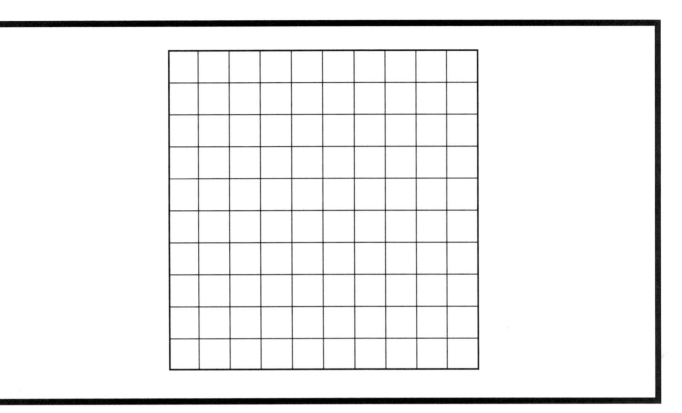

Shade 0.23 of the grid.

Gold beads are worth ten thousand, blue beads are worth one thousand, green beads are worth one hundred, red beads are worth ten, and purple beads are worth one.

Add together:

seventy-two thousand ninety-three and

forty-eight thousand six hundred eighty-one.

Write a word problem to go with this expression:

3 divided by $\frac{1}{3}$

_____

_____

_____

Draw a picture to go with your problem.

Draw a parallelogram with a 10-centimeter perimeter.

Write a story about pets.

Design a horizontal pictograph to go with it.

Draw a kennel full of dogs.

Make 20% of them black.

Make 10% of the dogs white.

Make 30% of the dogs tan.

What fraction of the dogs is another color? _____

Draw pictures representing three fractions that are greater than $\frac{1}{4}$ and less than $\frac{2}{3}$.

Write a story about sports.

Design a vertical pictograph to go with it.

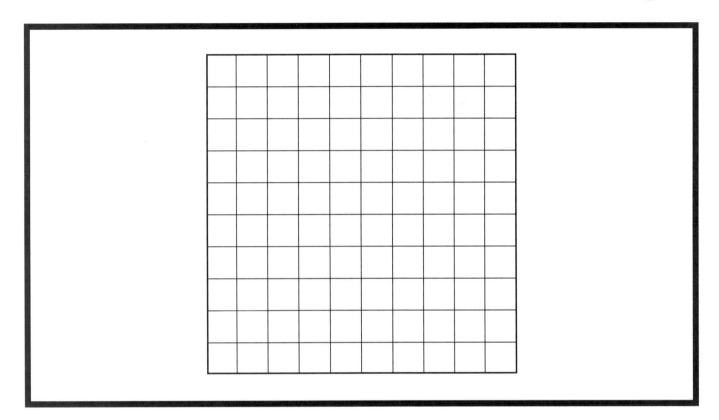

Shade $\frac{3}{5}$ of the grid so that no fifth touches another.

Write a story about money spent for food.

Draw a circle graph to go with it.

_____

_____

_____

_____

_____

_____

_____

[blank work box]

Create your own symbols for ten thousand, one thousand, one hundred, ten, and one.

Using your symbols, show and add together:

forty-five thousand nine hundred thirteen and

sixty thousand two hundred ninety-five.

Write a word problem to go with this equation.

$$\frac{5}{8} - \frac{1}{4} = \underline{\hspace{1.5cm}}$$

_____

_____

_____

Draw a picture to go with your problem.

Kevin has 20 marbles. 25% of them are blue. The rest are red.
Zach says 20% of his marbles are red. He has the same number
of marbles as Kevin has. How many of his marbles are blue?

How many one-foot-square tiles do you need to cover a
6-foot by 8-foot area of floor? _____

Design a pattern using 2 different colors of tile.

Tiles of the same color cannot be placed next to one another.

Choose three different animals. Create a Venn diagram
to show how they are alike and how they are different.

Design a flag for a mythical country. Use as many geometric shapes as you can.

Explain the symbols on your flag.

Divide the box above in half.

On the left side, make a picture of a fraction that is greater than three fourths.

On the right side, make a picture of a fraction that is less than three fourths.

Gold beads are worth ten thousand, blue beads are worth one thousand, green beads are worth one hundred, red beads are worth ten, and purple beads are worth one.

Add together:

three thousand eight hundred seventy-two and

ninety-six thousand five hundred seventeen.

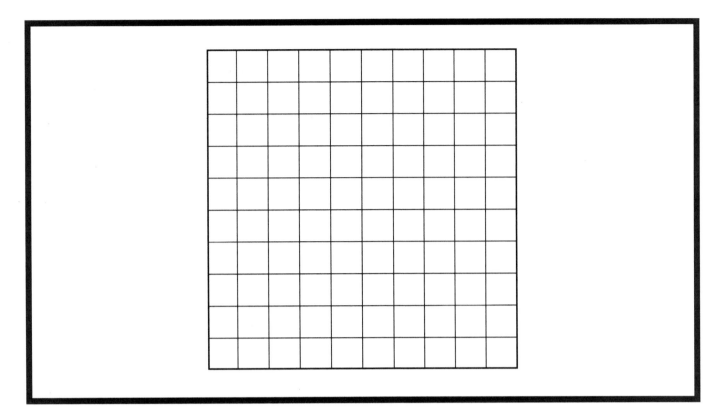

Draw a 10–by–10 grid.

Shade $\frac{1}{5}$ of it.

Draw a rectangle with a 5-inch base. Shade 0.20 of it.

Create a Venn diagram about the balls used in
four different sports.

The Venn diagram should show what those balls have
in common and how they are different.

Assign a certain place value to different shapes.

Using those shapes, show two numbers with a value greater than ten thousand, and add them together.

Draw a fruit orchard.

10% of the trees are apple trees.

20% of the trees are peach trees.

The rest are plum trees.

Draw cars in a parking lot.

0.25 of the cars are blue.

0.50 of the cars are green.

Write the decimal which represents the cars that are neither green nor blue.

On a circle graph, show 0.25, 0.35, and 0.40.

Write a story to go with your graph.

_____

_____

_____

_____

On a number line show 0, $\frac{1}{4}$, $2\frac{1}{2}$, $3\frac{3}{4}$, and 5.

Write a story to go with your number line.

_____

_____

_____

_____

Make a picture of a dog that weighs ten pounds.

Make a picture of an animal that weighs $\frac{1}{2}$ what the dog weighs.

Make a picture of an animal that weighs $\frac{1}{8}$ what the dog weighs.

Make a picture of an animal that weighs about $\frac{1}{3}$ of what the dog weighs.

Tell how much each animal weighs.

Design a pattern where size and shape are the same and color varies.

Make a design using 4 octagons, 3 triangles, and 2 quadrilaterals.
Make your design symmetrical.

Design 3 different sheets of stickers whose total worth is $5.30.